Published by Ladybird Books Ltd
80 Strand, London, WC2R 0RL
A Penguin Company

001
© LADYBIRD BOOKS LTD MMVIII
This edition MMXIV
LADYBIRD and the device of a Ladybird are trademarks of Ladybird Books Ltd

ISBN: 978-0-72329-773-4

Printed in China

Ladybird
Stories for 5 year olds

Written by Joan Stimson
Illustrated by Debora Van de Leijgraff

Mervyn's glasses

It was morning. Like all night birds, Mr and Mrs Owl were preparing for bed.

"I'm worried about Mervyn," said Mrs Owl. "I don't think he can see very well."

"You worry too much," said Mr Owl.
He snuggled up to his wife. "Mervyn's just fine. You get a good day's sleep."

The Owl family slept all day. At dusk they woke up, and Mr Owl flew off to work.

That night Mrs Owl watched Mervyn carefully. She was right. Mervyn couldn't see well. He didn't always empty his plate. He held his new book too close to his eyes.

At bedtime Mrs Owl spoke to her husband again. "Tomorrow, you must fly over to Mr Specs," she said. "He'll soon put Mervyn right."

When Mervyn woke up, Mrs Owl explained the plan.

"But I don't want to wear glasses," said Mervyn.
"They'll fall down my beak. They'll make me look silly."

"You'll look very handsome," said Mrs Owl.
"Your father wears glasses and there's nothing
wrong with his looks!"

"But Dad's old," said Mervyn. Then he blushed.
He didn't want to offend his parents.

Mervyn enjoyed the visit to Mr Specs. Mr Specs tested his eyes with all kinds of charts and lenses.

"This is fun," thought Mervyn.
He liked sorting out
the shapes and colours.

The next week he went to collect his glasses. He looked in Mr Specs' mirror, and saw himself clearly for the first time. "What a fine bird I am!" he thought. "But I don't like my glasses."

9

On the way home Mervyn noticed all kinds of new things.

"Look at the stars. See those glow worms," he shouted. "These glasses work a treat."

But when he got home, Mervyn caught sight of himself in the mirror. "Silly old glasses!" he said to himself, stomping up and down his branch crossly.

At that moment the postman arrived. "Special delivery," he said, and handed Mervyn a letter.

"What lovely big writing," said Mervyn.
"It's an invitation," he told his parents. "To David's party. But I'm not going... not in these glasses!"

All week Mr and Mrs Owl tried to persuade Mervyn. "Please go to the party," they said. "All your friends will be there. You don't want to disappoint David."

On the night of the party, Mervyn's parents tried one last time.

Mervyn shook his head.

"Well," said Dad. "If you don't want to play games and win prizes and eat a party tea, then that's up to you. I only wish I could go!"

Mervyn started to think about all the other owls having fun. In the end, he decided to go to David's party. He brushed his feathers and wrapped the present.

Then he flew there – all by himself.

David was waiting on his branch to greet Mervyn.

Mervyn landed gracefully and held out the present. When he looked up shyly, he got a really super surprise!

David was wearing glasses, too.
And he looked really cool!

The queue

It was Monday morning. The doctor's waiting room was full. The patients were trying to be patient. The nurse gave them each a number, to show their place in the queue.

Number one was a tortoise. He held a tissue to his nose. "I dink it's a cold," he sniffed.

Number two was a cat. She rubbed the fur near her tummy. "I ate too much," she groaned.

Number three was a rabbit.
One long ear was wrapped in
a bandage.
"I hate earache," she
complained. "It hurts to hop."

Number four was a small dog.
His leg was in a splint.
"It must be better for Sports
Day," he yapped.

Number five was a mouse. She didn't look at all well.

The tortoise, the cat, the rabbit and the dog all stared at the mouse. The nurse peeked through her window. "I think it's... don't-want-to-go-to-school-itis," whispered the mouse.

The patients looked shocked. The nurse smiled.

"In that case," said the nurse, "Number five can go in first."

"Good idea!" said the tortoise, the cat, the rabbit and the dog. "Someone with whatever-it-is-itis must see the doctor straight away!"

The up and down story

Mrs Kangaroo was on top of the world. She had a brand-new baby. The baby was called Clifford.

Mrs Kangaroo rang up her friend.
"Come and see my son," she said.

The friend hopped over right away. She had brought a big book on child care. "I can give you some tips as well," she said. "I've got three children of my own."

Mrs Kangaroo listened to her friend's advice. She read the book carefully. She wanted to be a good mother more than anything.

Clifford settled down quickly. He slept at night. He gurgled through the day.

"Being a mum is easy," thought Mrs Kangaroo. "It's time to get out and about." She telephoned her friend. "We'll hop over for coffee," she said.

Mrs Kangaroo dressed Clifford in his best clothes and popped him in her pouch. She set off at top speed.

But before she got to the end of the road, Clifford started wailing. He'd never made that dreadful noise before. Whatever could be the matter?

Mrs Kangaroo lifted Clifford out of her pouch. She remembered everything she had read in the book.

She checked Clifford carefully, but he was clean and dry. He didn't have wind.

Suddenly Mrs Kangaroo noticed Clifford's face. It wasn't kangaroo-coloured at all. Clifford's face was bright green!

Mrs Kangaroo was alarmed. Clifford must have the horrible disease the book had mentioned. It was called travel sickness and it affected very young kangaroos.

Sadly, Mrs Kangaroo tiptoed the rest of the way to her friend's. She went as smoothly as she could, but it was difficult for a kangaroo not to hop at all.

23

By the time Mrs Kangaroo arrived, Clifford was in bad shape. His mother needed that cup of coffee.

"It's nothing to worry about," said the friend. "Get some Bouncewell medicine."

Mrs Kangaroo went straight to the chemist's and bought some. "Put a teaspoonful in Clifford's next bottle," advised the chemist.

After Clifford's feed Mrs Kangaroo set off for the shops. But the medicine didn't work. Clifford wailed all afternoon.

When she got home, Mrs Kangaroo rang her friend. "That medicine is no good," she complained. "Clifford's all green again and I don't know what to do."

"Clifford will grow out of it," said the friend. "Lots of babies get travel sickness."

But Mrs Kangaroo couldn't wait for Clifford to grow out of it. She didn't want to be stuck at home all day. Being a mum wasn't so easy after all. Someone should have warned her.

Crossly, Mrs Kangaroo began to turn out her cupboards. Suddenly she found her old roller skates. She got very excited. Could this be the answer to Clifford's problems?

The next day Mrs Kangaroo took Clifford for a trial run.
She crossed her fingers for luck.

Wheeeee... Mrs Kangaroo soon got the
hang of her skates again. Clifford had
never had such a smooth ride.

In no time at all Mrs Kangaroo was halfway across town. The baby's face was still a beautiful kangaroo colour and Mum wasn't stuck at home.

But Mrs Kangaroo was careful not to skate past the police station. She would hate to get arrested for speeding!

29

INTELLIGENT ANIMALS

KINGFISHER

First published 2018 by Kingfisher
an imprint of Macmillan Children's Books
20 New Wharf Road, London N1 9RR
Associated companies throughout the world
www.panmacmillan.com

Series editor: Hayley Down
Design: Jeni Child

ISBN 978-0-7534-4233-3

Copyright © Macmillan Publishers International Ltd 2018

9 8 7 6 5 4 3 2 1

1TR/0717/WKT/UG/128MA

A CIP catalogue record for this book is available from the British Library.

Printed in China

Picture credits
The Publisher would like to thank the following for permission to reproduce their material.
Top = t; Bottom = b; Middle = m; Left = l; Right = r
Front cover: iStock/davidevison; Back cover: iStock/clintspencer; Cover flap: iStock/ erhandayi; Page 1 Shutterstock/Paul Hampton; 3 iStock/isuaneye; 4–5 iStock/ jag_cz; 4m iStock/zsv3207, 4b Shutterstock/Rudmer Zwerver; 5t iStock/Shongololo90, 5b iStock markrhiggins; 6 iStock/RyanDeanMorrison; 7t iStock/ezeePics Studio, 7b iStock/abzerit; 8–9 Getty/Luis Castaneda; 10–11 iStock/zsv3207, 10b iStock/Konrad Wothe/Minden Pictures, 11t iStock/TheSP4NISH, 11b Alamy/Km Petersen; 12 (1) Alamy/Waterframe; 13 (2) Nature Picture Library/Jane Burton, 13 (3) iStock/Zoran Kolundja, 13 (4) Shutterstock/Andrew Korson, 13 (5) Alamy/ Adriane Van Zandbergen, 13 (6) iStock/EzumeImages, 13 (7) Alamy/blickwinkel, 13 (8) Getty/Richard Du Toit, 13 (9) Alamy/imageBROKER, 13 (10) Shutterstock/ Reptiles4all; 14t Alamy/AndyHammer, 14m Creative Commons; 15t Alamy/blickwinkel, 15m iStock/Uwe bergwitz; 16–17 Getty/Jim Abernethy, 16b Shuterstock. kudla, 17m iStock/Snowleopard1; 18 Alamy/ARCTIC IMAGES; 19t Alamy/B. A. E. Inc., 19b iStoc/gmccoop; 20–21 Alamy/GM Photo Images; 22t Shutterstock/Ryan M. Bolton, 22bl Getty/The Washington Post, 22br Alamy/Nature Picture Library; 23t Alamy/Worldfptp, 23bl Alamy/Paul Oliviera, 23br Alamy/Arterra Picture Library; 24–25 iStock/Eel_Tony; 26–27 Alamy/blickwinkel; 27t iStock/steveo73, 28b iStock/jez_bennett; 29t iStock/JasonPrince; 29m iStock/Utopia_88, 29b iStock/jez_bennett; 30 (1) iStock/Tammy616; 31 (2) iStock/GP232, 31 (3) Istock/kojihirano, 31 (4) iStock/hphimagelibrary, 31 (5) Shutterstock/Edwin Butter, 31 (6) Shutterstock/Rudmer Zwerver, 31 (7) iStock/mariusz_prusacyk, 31 (8) iStock/truog, 31 (9) Alamy/Rolf Nussbaumer Photography, 31 (10) Alamy/Cultura RM; 32– 33 Getty/Wayne Lynch; 34–35 iStock/worakit; 36 Getty/Anup Shah; 37t iStock/ANDREYGUDKOV, 37b Alamy/Sergey Uryadnikov; 38–39 Alamy/robertharding, 39t iStock/PinkPython, 39b ALamy/Shotshop GmbH; 40–41 Alamy/National Geographic Creative; 42t Shutterstock/Andrew Astbury, 42bl iStock/MivPiv, 42br iStock/ BirdImages; 43t iStock/milehightraveler, 43bliStock/kjekol. 43br Alamy/Barbara Gardener; 45t iStock/Kerrick, 45m Alamy/Arterra Picture Library, 45b iStock/ thatreec; 46 (1) Getty/Suzi Esterhas; 47 (2) iStock/dptro, 47 (3) iStock/Yann-HUBERT, 47 (4) iStock/jonathonfilskov-photography, 47 (5) iStock/nikamata, 47 (6) iStock/JohnPitcher, 47 (7) iStock/Shonogolo90, 47 (8) Alamy/ImagesBROKER, 47 (9) Shutterstock/gilkop, 47 (10) Shutterstock/Katherine Bennett; 48–49 Alamy/ Minden Pictures; 50 Alamy/Nature picture Library; 51t iStock/GomezDavid, 51m iStock/markrhiggins, 51b Alamy/ Auscape International Pty Ltd; 52tl iStock/ Olesya22, 52tr iStock/GlobalP, 52bl Shutterstock/sakavichanka, 52br Shutterstock/Dmitry Kalinovsky; 53t iStock/CraigRJD, 53bl Shutterstock/StudioSmart, 53br Shutterstock/Glass and Nature; 54–55 iStock/GP232, 55 Shutterstock/Carolina Stratico; 56–57 Getty/Gunter Ziesler; 58 (1)iStock/Photocech; 52 (2) iStock/ KenCanning, 52 (3) iStock/pjmalsbury, 52 (4) Alamy/Minden Pictures, 52 (5) iStock/ANDREYGUDKOV, 52 (6) iStock/jeanro, 52 (7) Alamy/dpa picture alliance, 52 (8) iStock/Uwe-Bergwitz, 52 (9) iStock/NEALITPMCCLIMON, 52 (10) iStock/eco2drew; 60 iStock/OlgaLIS; 61 iStock/darios44; 62 iStock/SeanPavonePhoto; 63 iStock/ suefeldberg.

IN FOCUS

INTELLIGENT ANIMALS

BY CAMILLA DE LA BEDOYERE

KINGFISHER

CONTENTS

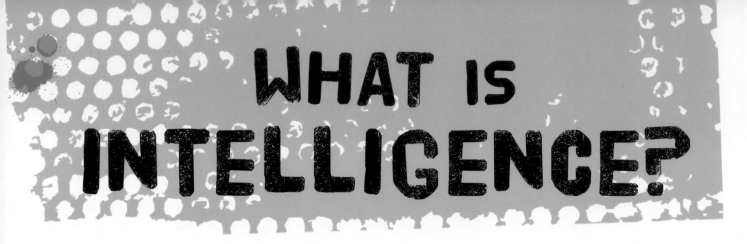

WHAT IS INTELLIGENCE?

How can we work out how clever animals are, when we are still trying to understand human **intelligence**? That's a question that scientists have been puzzling over for a long time. Deciding what makes an animal "clever" is one problem, but measuring that cleverness is just as tricky!

We can never get inside the head of a parrot or a gorilla, so we don't know how it makes decisions, how it plans or what it feels. One thing we do know, is that animals are as clever as they need to be to carry out their amazing life stories, some of which you will discover in this book.

red squirrel raiding bird feeder

INSIDE YOU'LL FIND ...

... animals that learn

Learning means **DISCOVERING** new things, from experience or being taught. Dogs learn commands and chimps learn how to use tools. Orang-utans have even learned how to wash with soap by copying people!

Communication means **TALKING** to each other. Animals don't use words in the same way as we do, but they have other ways to communicate. Ring-tailed lemurs use smells, and dolphins use clicks and whistles.

... smart talkers

... big brains

Brain size matters. Generally, a **BIG BRAIN** in relation to the size of the body suggests an animal is clever. Monkeys and apes (including humans) have relatively big brains.

7

SUPER
SENSES

BRAIN POWER

An animal's brain is the place that receives information and controls the body. An animal gets information about its surroundings from its senses. That information is carried by **nerves** to the brain, usually in the animal's head.

The brain controls the way an animal reacts to the information it receives, such as deciding to run away from danger. Generally, intelligent animals have bigger brains that can process the information in a more complex way than "simpler" animals. That means they have more options for how they will react.

instincts

Some **REACTIONS** are **instinctive**. This means they happen without any learning. All animals are born with instincts and they are essential for survival.

Male bowerbirds, for example, have an instinct to collect colourful objects and build a beautiful bower to impress females. However, they can learn how and where to find the best decorations.

SMART FACT

Will this hamster sense danger?

invertebrates

An invertebrate is an animal without a **BACKBONE**. This group includes bugs, crabs and octopuses. Invertebrates have nerves and senses, but not all of them have brains. They rely on instinct to survive and are not often thought of as "intelligent".

Vertebrates are animals with a backbone and a **BRAIN**. They include fish, amphibians, reptiles, birds and mammals. Thanks to their brain, they are more likely to learn and adapt their behaviour to suit new situations. Mammals and birds can learn and communicate in especially impressive ways.

vertebrates

SENSE-ATIONS!

Animals understand the world around them using their **senses**: sight, hearing touch, smell and taste.

1 Sight: huge eyes

Mantis shrimps are invertebrates with large eyes and incredible vision. They can see colours that are invisible to us and other mammals.

2 Sight: mirrors

Cats, big and small, have a mirror-layer in their eyes that reflects light. It means they can hunt at night when their prey can't see them.

3 Hearing: ears

Good hearing helps a fennec fox find insects burrowing in the desert sand. Big ears help to "catch" sounds.

4 Hearing: holes

Drum-like ears behind a female frog's eyes are used to hear the call of a male from more than 1 kilometre away.

5 Touch: whiskers

The whiskers on a seal's face are useful for sensing touch underwater, and the movement of air on land. This helps the seal hunt and avoid danger.

6 Touch: hairs

A spider's whole body is covered in super-sensitive hairs that detect vibration and the slightest movement of air.

7 Smell: antennae

Antennae are long, sensitive body parts. A male hawkmoth's antennae smell the scent of a female, even if she is far away.

8 Smell: snout

The long, twitching snout of an elephant shrew is very sensitive to touch and smell. It can detect tiny ants and termites under piles of leaves.

9 Taste: barbels

A catfish's fleshy whiskers are called barbels and they sense taste. It's a life-saving skill for a fish that hunts in dark, murky water.

10 Taste: tongue

A snake flicks its tongue to taste the air. It then touches its tongue to the top of its mouth, sending nerve signals to the brain.

Which sense-ation is your number one?

SOUND PICTURES

Did you know that animals can use sound to see?

BAT POWERS

Hunting at night is a challenge for most animals. With little more than the moonlight to help them see, nocturnal animals often rely on superb hearing, touch or smell to find food. Bats, however, use a special sense called **echolocation**, or sonar.

They make high-pitched (ultrasonic) sounds in their throat, but send them out through an oddly shaped nose instead of through their mouth. The sounds, or clicks, bounce off solid objects, such as insects or trees, and are echoed back to the bat.

Large ears help the bat to hear the echoes. They are used to create a "sound picture", which helps the **predator** fly safely through the darkness and snatch insects out of the air.

SMART FACT

BLOOD-DRINKING VAMPIRE bats have another extra-special sense. They can detect the heat given out by an animal's blood as it flows just beneath the surface of the skin. Yikes!

vampire bat

DOLPHIN TALK

Marine predators may have to travel far through the ocean to find food. Light doesn't pass easily through water, so colours and shapes are not always visible, especially where the water is cloudy.

Dolphins use echolocation to overcome these problems. They make ultrasonic clicks by passing air through "lips" inside their nose to form sounds.

The sounds, or clicks, bounce off the dolphin's skull and pass through a round fatty area, called the "melon". This focuses the clicks into a beam that is directed at fish. When the sounds hit the fish's body, they create echoes that bounce back to the dolphin. Dolphins have a big, complex brain, so they can use this information to work out the size, position, speed and even type of **prey** they are chasing.

SMART FACT

RIVER DOLPHINS use sonar to find fish in murky slow-flowing waters. They have very poor eyesight, so they rely totally on their sound-seeing skills to survive in rivers, such as the Amazon.

river dolphin

SECRET SUPER POWERS

Your questions about some stunning skills answered.

Can some fish use electricity?

Yes, some can! Electric eels from the Amazon are the most deadly. They generate electricity in their body and release mega-bolts of shocks in the water. Their prey includes fish and frogs, but these 3-metre-long predators produce enough electricity to kill humans.

Why do sharks have a spotty nose?

A shark's nose is covered with tiny holes, not spots, and they are key to a shark's hunting success. Each hole leads to a sense organ that detects the electricity made by another animal's muscles. A shark can sense tiny amounts of electricity and uses this skill to find prey, even flatfish lying still on the seabed!

Why are snakes so deadly?

Many snakes have **venomous** fangs, but that's not the only reason they are supreme predators. Pit vipers have heat-sensitive organs, called pits, between their eyes and their nostrils, which detect the heat given off by their prey, such as small rodents. That means they can hunt in the dark and find prey that is **camouflaged**.

MAGNETIC MIGRATORS

The Earth's **magnetic field** is generated by molten rock in its core. We use the magnetic field to find north, south, east and west – unlike us, migrating animals don't need a compass!

Many birds **MIGRATE**, or travel, huge distances to reach feeding or nesting sites. How they find their way is still a bit of a mystery, but the ability to detect **magnetism** seems to play an important part in this impressive skill.

Young **MIGRATING** birds tend to follow older, more experienced birds but they soon learn to look out for – and recognize – useful route-markers, such as mountains and coasts.

Although birds can learn migration routes, they also use instinct. **CUCKOOS** are not raised by their parents, but they still know where and when to migrate.

Scientists have found crystals of **MAGNETITE** – a mineral that is used to make magnets – inside birds' beaks.

ARCTIC TERNS take on one of the world's most incredible **migrations** – from near the North Pole to the Antarctic and back again. They navigate up to 96,000 kilometres in a single year!

TERMITES can also detect the Earth's magnetic field. They use it to build their tall, thin mounds with the widest sides facing east and west. The shape helps to control the mound's temperature. The wide parts of the mound catch the sunlight in the morning and evening, keeping the mound warm, but in the scorching-hot afternoon, the sun is high over the narrow roof of the mound and doesn't overheat the termites inside.

Scientists think many other animals, including **RAINBOW TROUT** and **HONEYBEES**, use this remarkable magnetic sense to find their way.

SMART
SURVIVORS

TRICKS

How much intelligence does it take these animals to catch their prey?

ALLIGATOR SNAPPING TURTLE

This beast hides in rivers with opens jaws, waggling a long, red tongue that looks like a worm. Fish and frogs try to eat the "worm", then the turtle lives up to its name and snaps its mouth shut around them! This isn't a planned attack; the turtle acts on instinct. When it feels something in its mouth, its instinct is to snap it shut – with a tasty result!

snap, snap, yum, yum!

NET-CASTING SPIDER

Many spiders build complex webs, but net-casting spiders hold a silken web between two legs and cast it, like a net, over their prey. Spiders are more intelligent than many invertebrates, with mini "brains" that are so big they spread into their legs. However, their hunting skills appear to be instinctive, not learned.

in the net

AND TRAPS

AMAZING ARCHERFISH

Archerfish live underwater, but their prey fly above the water's surface. These fish shoot a jet of water to knock a flying insect out of the air and into the water, where it can be gobbled up. Archerfish act on instinct, but with practice – and by watching other fish fail or succeed – they learn how to get better at hitting fast-moving bugs.

HUMPBACK WHALE

When humpback whales make a fishnet out of bubbles, they are using a trick they have learned from other whales. A group of whales blows bubbles of air as they swim in circles around a shoal of fish. The bubble net traps the fish, then the whales swim upwards, mouth open, through the net to eat the fish.

brilliant bubbles

great shot!

CLOSE UP

IN FOR THE KILL

Bears are adaptable animals, which means they can change their behaviour to suit their needs. Scientists believe this is a sign of considerable intelligence. Brown bears have learned that if they stand in a river, facing downstream, migrating salmon will leap right into their mouth! A successful bear can catch up to 100 salmon every day. Genius!

More about bears

Fish is full of protein and fat, which the bear stores in its body to help it survive a long, cold winter when food is scarce. Brown bears hibernate during the coldest weather.

ANIMALS THAT AMBUSH

Your questions answered about how animals use stealth and cunning to kill.

Do animals plan their attacks?

Polar bears know that seals pop their head up through ice holes to breathe. They prepare for a seal's appearance by lying patiently next to a hole for hours at a time. They are planning an attack, which will be over in seconds but which will provide calorie-rich food for the bear and her cubs.

Why are great white sharks so scary?

Great white sharks are possibly the most intelligent sharks, and that makes them deadly. They swim in deep, dark water, where their victims can't see them and then, when the time is right, launch into a fast swim upwards, jaws wide open. Their prey (usually a seal) is taken by surprise and has no time to swim to safety.

Do spiders use intelligence to kill?

Crab spiders are so well camouflaged that they can hide on a flower and ambush any flies or bees that come visiting. They are using instinct, not intelligence, to ambush their prey. Their colour and shape are so perfect for the task of hiding them that they don't need to plan an attack. Crab spiders just have to wait for lunch to come to them!

crocodile ambushing wildebeest

Are crocodiles clever?

The crocodiles that hunt wildebeest crossing the Mara River in Africa appear to be cleverer than most! These crocs know where the migrating animals cross the river every year, and work together in groups to ambush them. The crocs choose a victim, then block its route. Once surrounded, there is no escape and the crocodiles attack.

PACKS AND PRIDES

Hunting as a group is a smart move when it means you can catch much bigger prey than you could catch by yourself. Here are some incredible predators that have truly mastered the art of teamwork, and use it to deadly effect. They may not be successful every time they hunt, but the rewards are great when they are – just one kill may provide enough food for the whole group. Hunting packs and prides rely on intelligence and communication to succeed. While the adults do the hard work, youngsters watch and learn.

lions attacking
a wildebeest

sharing jobs

LIONESSES work as a team to hunt large animals such as zebras and wildebeest. While the females hunt, the males stay with the cubs. A group of lions is called a pride.

AFRICAN WILD DOGS are supreme hunters that combine speed with pack-power. They spread out to chase their prey, calling with yaps and barks to coordinate their attack.

pack power

smart strategy

SPOTTED HYENAS hunt their prey in packs, which are led by females. They are very intelligent animals and by working together they can catch a zebra four times the size of one hyena.

29

DEFENCE STRATEGIES

Instinct, physical traits or just pure cleverness – which defence strategies work best?

1 Clever camouflage

A camouflaged animal uses colour and pattern to blend into its surroundings. Look closely – can you spot the seahorse?

2. Blurred lines

A zebra's stripes make it stand out when it's alone. When a zebra runs, or is in a herd, the stripes blur its outline and confuse predators.

3. Hot spot!

Bees mob hungry hornets that threaten their colony. They beat their wings to raise the temperature – until the heat kills the invader!

4. Black lemurs

Black lemurs chew giant millipedes to make them release **chemicals**. Lemurs paste their fur with the pulp – it's a homemade bug-repellent!

5. Take aim!

Some howler monkeys have learned to throw branches from the treetops at predators prowling around the ground below.

6. Danger drums

While rabbits are grazing, some keep a lookout. If they spot a predator, these rabbits thump the ground with their feet to warn their friends.

7. Warning calls

If a vervet monkey sees an eagle, it calls to its troop to take cover. If it sees a snake, it uses a different call to tell the troop to climb into a tree!

8. Mimic masters

A mimic octopus can change its appearance in a flash to fool predators. It can take on the colours and shapes of sea snakes, fish or jellyfish!

9. Play dead!

When a Virginia opossum is scared, and there's no place to run, it flips over, hangs out its tongue and pretends to be dead!

10. Stinky spray

Stinky skunks spray nasty smells at their enemies. Striped skunks do headstands, so they can spray farther and more accurately!

Which defence strategy is your number one?

SAFETY IN NUMBERS

Musk oxen are huge, shaggy-furred beasts that graze in herds. If they spy a pack of wolves, they move swiftly into an outward-facing circle, keeping their calves safe in the centre.

More about herds

Grazing animals, such as musk oxen, zebras, deer and antelopes, spend hours eating grass. Standing on an open plain leaves these animals vulnerable to attack, but when everyone is keeping an eye out for a predator, there's safety in numbers. Animals that live, feed or migrate in groups need to be alert to each other's alarm signals. Calls, whistles, tail flashes and sudden movements all warn other members of the group to flee.

LIVING TOGETHER

When a chimp grins and shows its teeth it is communicating fear or worry – like a human's nervous smile. If a chimp glares and opens its mouth, with its lips over its teeth, it is warning another chimp to stay away.

GO APE!

Great apes are our closest relatives. Like us they use tools, live and work together, talk and play

- A **"PANT-HOOT"** is a sound that chimps use to show they are happy or excited. Each chimp has its own pant-hoot, so other members of the family know who's talking, even in a dense, dark jungle.

- Chimps **KISS** to say "hello" and **HUG**, especially when they are feeling scared.

- **ORANG-UTANS** make beds from leaves and they use sticks to get insects out of their holes. Orang-utans are fast learners, and often learn by copying each other, or humans!

- **PLAYTIME** is an important part of a baby gorilla's day. Apes use play to learn how to live as part of a **GROUP**.

- Chimps and their cousins, **BONOBOS**, live in groups called troops. Like other primates, these apes spend lots of time grooming, stroking and touching one another. It helps them to form strong family bonds.

37

PARENTS that look after their families for many years have plenty of time to share knowledge and learning with them.

FAMILY LIFE

Baby elephants need their mothers. But their grandmothers, aunts, siblings and cousins all help with bringing up baby!

An elephant is one of the few animals that can **RECOGNIZE ITSELF** in a mirror. Most animals ignore their reflection, or think it's another animal.

DAUGHTERS often stay with their mother all their life. When elephants die, the other members of the family have been known to visit the place where the body lay, even years later.

Elephants **STROKE** and caress each other with their trunk. Mothers have been known to smack babies with their trunk!

A group of elephants is called a **HERD** and is led by the most senior female, called the matriarch. She knows all the best places to find food and she can remember where to find watering holes.

Elephants **COMMUNICATE** with soft sounds and loud trumpets, but they also make deep rumbles that travel long distances underground. Other elephants feel these rumbles through their feet.

A **BLUE WHALE** is about 20 times the size of an elephant, but its brain is less than twice as big. It's no wonder that elephants are regarded as among the most intelligent creatures on the planet.

An **ANGRY** elephant stares and flaps its ears before it begins to pace. In a split second, it may decide to charge. These are huge, powerful animals with a strong instinct to protect their family.

Elephants **TEACH** their young how to strip sticks from a tree and use them to swat flies away or scratch their back.

DANGER AT SEA

Orcas live in close family groups of about 30 for their entire life. They are nicknamed the "wolves of the sea", because their families, or pods, hunt like a pack of wolves. In this picture, a seal resting on an **ice floe** has no idea that a pod of orcas has decided to target it in an attack. Working together, the orcas create waves that rock the ice floe until it tips – and a final big wave sends the seal sliding down and into the mouth of a waiting orca.

More about orcas

Orcas are large dolphins and, like their smaller cousins, they have impressive brain power. Younger orcas watch and learn from a distance. When they are older, they will know what to do and can join the adults in an attack.

Arctic fox

CANINE CLANS

You've probably met a clever pet dog before, but did you know their relatives are intelligent too?

OUR BEST FRIEND

You probably know that domestic, or pet, dogs can be trained to sit, lie down and even fetch! But did you know that scientists have discovered the cleverest dogs can understand up to 250 human words? Domestic dogs have been bred by humans to have different skills, from hunting to herding sheep.

sheepdog

FOX FAMILIES

Foxes are superb survivors and very adaptable. Thanks to their intelligence they can change their behaviour to find and store food for the long winter, and they can live in a range of habitats. Some foxes live in small family groups, in dens, but Arctic foxes usually live alone.

fox and cubs

LONE WOLVES?

Wolves are the **ancestors** of all domestic dogs. They live in groups that are led by one pair of wolves. The adults share the task of looking after cubs and they hunt together. They carefully choose their victim before launching an attack and, if necessary, they quickly change their plan during the chase.

wolves in a pack

JACKALS

Jackals usually live in pairs – one male and one female – and mate for life. They share a large territory, which they defend from intruders. Young jackals are allowed to live with their parents until they establish their own territory. Until then, young jackals will help to raise their younger siblings.

home-makers

BODY TALK

Smiles, grimaces and frowns are three ways in which some animals, such as apes, show their feelings. When an animal uses its body to show its feelings, its behaviour is described as "body language". Humans and other apes are expert at it, but so are many other animals . . .

SMART FACT

When an animal **RuBS** its body against a plant it isn't just scratching an itch – it's spreading its smell about. The smell carries a message, telling other animals to stay away.

stay away!

44

I'm bored!

Animals **YAWN**, perhaps to show they are bored or tired. When one animal yawns, others can't stop themselves yawning too!

I give up!

BATTLES and playtimes often involve a winner and a loser. Dogs show they want to give up by rolling over and exposing their soft belly and throat. The winner backs off, and both animals are saved from injury.

get to work!

Animals can communicate using smelly chemicals called **PHEROMONES**. Ants use different pheromones to work together to build a nest from leaves, to warn each other when their nest is under attack, or to organize a team to defend the nest.

TOP 10

TALKERS

Animals can communicate using chemicals, smells, body language and a huge range of sounds.

 Talking parrots

Parrots can mimic human talking. Some parrots can even learn to use human words to describe things, such as colours!

2 Gorilla grunts

Wild gorillas use sound and body language to communicate, but scientists have taught some gorillas to use sign language too.

3 Whale song

The loudest song is sung by blue whales, but humpback whales sing the longest and most complex songs of any animal.

4 Cuddly critters

A prairie dog uses cuddles and kisses to communicate, but it can also use about 10 different barks to tell its family where danger lies.

5 Grasshopper chirps

A grasshopper communicates with chirps. It makes these loud sounds by rubbing its legs against its wings.

6 Coyote calls

A coyote can yip, howl or bark to its pack. The pack can probably recognize which family member is calling to them.

7 Chit chat

Meerkats purr when they're happy, chatter when they're nervous and squeal when they spot danger!

8 Marsh warbler

This bird can copy other birds' songs, learning up to 100 different tunes that it uses to compose its own melodies.

9 Wet whistlers

A bottlenose dolphin makes its own unique whistle. Scientists think these whistles are used in the same way as we use a name!

10 Queen calls

When death's head moths enter a beehive to steal honey, they make squeaks similar to those of a queen bee, so the bees ignore them!

Which animal would you like to talk to?

USING TOOLS

For a long time, it was thought that humans were the only animals that could make and use tools. In fact, many animals are able to use sticks, stones and other objects to make life easier. They may learn to use tools by trial and error, or they learn by watching other members of their species. Sometimes, the use of a tool is pure instinct, and doesn't need any learning at all.

capuchin monkey

SMART FACT

CAPUCHIN MONKEYS find heavy rocks and smash nuts with them. It's much quicker and easier than trying to crack a nut open with their teeth!

SEA OTTERS collect shellfish and rocks from the seabed. Then, floating on their back, they bash the shellfish with the rock to break it open.

otters rock!

chimp champions

A chimp pushes a stick into a termite mound and pulls it out when it's covered in termites. Chimps also make spears from sticks, which they use to hunt.

CROWS are among the most intelligent birds. They can pick up a stick in their beak and use it to poke food out of a hollow branch. They can even bend wire to make a hook!

clever crow

SURPRISE

RATS

Many **experiments** have been conducted to find out if rats are intelligent. In one experiment, two rats were placed in a pen, one free to roam and the other locked in a cell. The free rat unlocked its friend before eating the food in the pen. This suggests that rats care about each other.

rat race

PIGS

Scientists have been surprised to discover just how smart pigs are! One experiment involved placing food hidden from plain view, but visible reflected in mirrors around the pen. The pigs were able to use the mirrors to find the food within 23 seconds - easy peasy!

big squeal

SMARTIES

Don't underestimate these animals; they are smarter than you might think...

INSECTS

Social insects, such as bees, wasps, ants and termites, live as colonies with complex social structures. It's common for social insects to leave all the egg-laying to one female, called the queen. Workers care for eggs and larvae, and fetch food, while soldiers protect the **colony** from attack.

clever bees

COCKATOOS

Unlike crows, most birds are not smart enough to make tools. Figaro, a Goffin's cockatoo, is an exception! He sculpted a tool out of wood and used it to pull food from hard-to-reach spots. This amazed scientists, who later discovered that Figaro could teach other cockatoos his new trick!

bird brain

ANIMAL SCHOOL

Your questions answered about how animals learn.

Can animals count?

They may not understand numbers the same way we do, but some animals do seem to count. Rats, members of the crow family, parrots and apes all seem to understand ideas about numbers such as quantities, or amounts, including "more" and "fewer".

Why is playtime useful for learning?

Like children, animals, such as lion cubs, can learn by playing. It gives them a chance to practise hunting, running and climbing – all skills that they need to survive. Clever youngsters like to investigate the world around them. This may help them to develop problem-solving skills.

Do animal parents teach their children?

Some youngsters can learn just by watching their parents, but it appears that some adults take time to show their young what to do. Meerkat adults show their pups how to kill a scorpion and remove its deadly sting before eating it. Orca mothers take their calves to waters where baby grey whales are born, and show the calves how to make their first kill.

Can wild animals help us?

Yes! If you visit Laguna Beach in Brazil, you might spot wild dolphins and local fishermen working side by side to catch fish. The dolphins herd the fish towards the fishermen and signal with their fins when the fishermen should cast their nets. This has been happening for many generations; the dolphins teach their young how to help, keeping the tradition going!

CLOSE UP

LEARNING WITH ANIMALS

Scientists who want to work out how clever animals are, and how they behave, are called **ethologists**. There is so much more to discover about the incredible creatures we share our planet with. It's important we protect animals and save their habitats so they can live their natural life. And while they do that, we can enjoy watching them – and using our brilliant brain power to try and understand their brilliant brain power!

Would you like to study animal behaviour?

If you want to find out how intelligent an animal is, how would you create an experiment? An experiment must not harm the animal in any way. Some of the best animal scientists in history have been the ones who are happy to sit and watch animals behaving naturally, and think about what they are doing, and why. So find some time to watch animals. Take photos, draw pictures and record your observations and what you have learned.

ANIMALS IN DANGER

Many clever creatures are in deadly peril, and in danger of becoming **extinct**. Humans threaten their survival, but are we clever enough to save them?

1

Tigers

There are fewer than 3200 of these magnificent cats in the wild. People hunt them for their fur and the tigers face losing their habitat.

Elephants

These mighty, incredibly clever beasts are hunted for the ivory in their tusks. All types of elephant are now endangered.

Spix's macaw

Macaws and other parrots are taken from the jungle to be sold as pets. Spix's macaws have not been seen in the wild since 2000.

African wild dog

Humans hunt this intelligent animal and it is losing its habitat to farmers. There are fewer than 1500 adults left.

River dolphins

The Yangtze river dolphin is probably extinct already. River dolphins are threatened by hunting and pollution.

Kakapo

Scientists work hard to protect the last 160 or so kakapos – large flightless parrots – on three islands near New Zealand.

Amur leopard

This cat's beautiful fur makes it a target for hunters. There are probably no more than 60 of these Amur leopards left in the wild.

Great apes

All of our closest ape cousins face an uncertain future, but none more so than mountain gorillas. There are about 880 of them left.

Blue whale

Following worldwide hunting, many whales faced extinction. Most hunting is now banned, but blue whales are not out of danger yet.

Red wolf

All wild red wolves had died by 1980. Scientists have released captive ones to create a new wild population of just 50 animals.

Which endangered animal is your number one?

THE INTELLIGENT ANIMALS QUIZ

Are you an expert on intelligent animals? Test your knowledge by completing this quiz! When you've answered all of the questions, turn to page 63 to find your score.

 1 Which of these animals is a vertebrate?
a) Dolphin
b) Octopus
c) Spider

 2 Which word means natural behaviour that is not learned?
a) Instant
b) Instinct
c) Intelligence

 3 Which of these tool-users doesn't use a stick to get food?
a) Chimp
b) Crow
c) Sea otter

 4 Which animals are described as canines?
a) Bears
b) Cats
c) Dogs

 5 What does a snake use to taste the air?
a) Its brain and its skin
b) Its tongue and its brain
c) Its tongue and its skin

 6 Which animals use echolocation to find their prey?
a) Bats
b) Parrots
c) Rabbits

 7 How many different tunes might a marsh warbler know?
a) More than 1000
b) More than 100
c) Up to 100

 8 Which smart mammals are called "wolves of the sea"?
a) Elephants
b) Orcas
c) Walruses

 9 Arctic terns go on long journeys. What are the journeys called?
a) Mega-flights
b) Migrations
c) Safaris

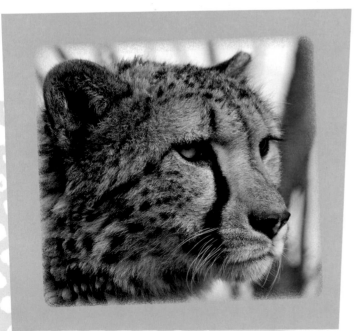